This book belongs to

Dillon

Useful words

(in the order they appear in this book)

dinosaur

eyes   teeth   legs

paint   daffodils   dandelions

dog   paper

Dippy Duck's
Dinosaur

Moira Andrew

Dippy Duck drew a dancing dinosaur. She drew all day, from dawn till dusk. But the dinosaur didn't look right.

The next day, Dippy Duck added dots all over the dinosaur's body. But the dinosaur still didn't look right.

So Dippy Duck drew deep dark eyes and dazzling teeth and dumpy legs to dance with. But the dinosaur still didn't look right.

"What shall I do?" she asked

Poor Peter.

"Paint is what you need, Dippy

Duck. Pots and pots of paint!"

said Poor Peter.

So Dippy Duck painted the dinosaur. She painted it with pink dots and purple dots and green dots.

Dippy Duck painted so many

dots that she felt quite dizzy!

She painted daffodils and

dandelions so the dinosaur

could dance in them.

Lucy Lamp Lady came to look

at the painting.

"My dinosaur still looks dreadful,"

said Dippy Duck sadly.

"He looks lonely," said Lucy Lamp Lady.

So Dippy Duck added the dinosaur's dad and a little dog.

Suddenly, there was a dreadful roar. The dinosaur jumped out of his picture and danced across the floor.

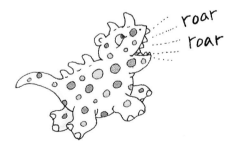
roar
roar

The dinosaur's dad danced and his little dog danced, too.

"Dance with us, Dippy Duck!"

they said. And she did.

Poor Peter and Lucy Lamp Lady

danced too. They danced till they

dropped.

The next day, Dippy Duck took

another piece of paper. She drew

all day, from dawn till dusk.

She drew ...

Well, what do you think she

drew? You decide!

The Letterlanders

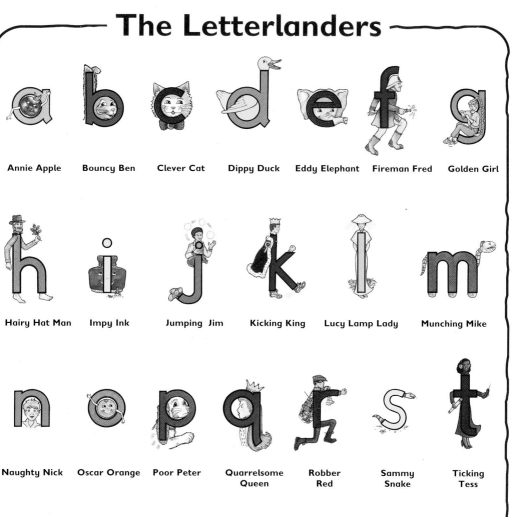

Annie Apple Bouncy Ben Clever Cat Dippy Duck Eddy Elephant Fireman Fred Golden Girl

Hairy Hat Man Impy Ink Jumping Jim Kicking King Lucy Lamp Lady Munching Mike

Naughty Nick Oscar Orange Poor Peter Quarrelsome Queen Robber Red Sammy Snake Ticking Tess

Uppy Umbrella Vase of Violets Wicked Water Witch Max and Maxine Yo-yo Man Zig Zag Zebra

This edition produced for
The Book People Ltd., Hall Wood Avenue,
Haydock, St. Helens WA11 9UL

Published by Collins Educational
An imprint of HarperCollins*Publishers* Ltd
77-85 Fulham Palace Road
London W6 8JB

First published 1998
Reprinted 1998

ISBN 0 00 303377 5

LETTERLAND® is a registered trademark of Lyn Wendon.

The author asserts the moral right to be identified as the author of this work.

British Library Cataloguing in Publication Data
A catalogue record for this book is available from the British Library.

Written by Moira Andrew
Illustrated by Sara Silcock (Linda Rogers Associates)
Designed by Michael Sturley
Consultant: Lyn Wendon, originator of Letterland

Printed by Printing Express, Hong Kong